The Best of
George Gershwin
and Ira Gershwin

The Best of George Gershwin and Ira Gershwin

WARNER BROS. PUBLICATIONS - THE GLOBAL LEADER IN PRINT
USA: 15800 NW 48th Avenue, Miami, FL 33014

WARNER/CHAPPELL MUSIC

CANADA: 40 SHEPPARD AVE. WEST, SUITE 800
TORONTO, ONTARIO M2N 6K9
SCANDINAVIA: P.O. BOX 533, VENDEVAGEN 85 B
S-182 15, DANDERYD, SWEDEN
AUSTRALIA: P.O. BOX 353
3 TALAVERA ROAD, NORTH RYDE N.S.W. 2113

Nuova CARISCH SRL.

ITALY: VIA CAMPANIA, 12
(ZONA INDUSTRIALE SESTO ULTERIANO)
20098 SAN GIULIANO MILANESE, MILANO
SPAIN: NUEVA CARISCH ESPANA, S.L.
MAGALLANES 25, 28015 MADRID
FRANCE: CARISCH FRANCE, SARL
20, RUE DE LA VILLE-L'EVEQUE,
75008 PARIS
www.carisch.com

INTERNATIONAL MUSIC PUBLICATIONS LIMITED

ENGLAND: GRIFFIN HOUSE,
161 HAMMERSMITH ROAD, LONDON W6 8BS
GERMANY: MARSTALLSTR. 8. D-80539 MUNCHEN
DENMARK: DANMUSIK, VOGNMAGERGADE 7
DK 1120 KOBENHAVNK

First published 1976
© Introduction Edward Lea 1976
INTERNATIONAL MUSIC PUBLICATIONS LIMITED

All Rights Reserved

Cover Montage Photography
and Book Design: Peter White

The Best of George Gershwin and Ira Gershwin

George Gershwin

George Gershwin

"Whenever he entered a room, he captured it instantly and completely, not because he was overbearing but because he had an irresistible, infectious vitality, an overwhelming personal magnetism beyond that of most of the greatest movie stars." This observation about George Gershwin was once made by Ira Gershwin's wife, Leonore.

The songs in this folio are evidence of Gershwin's remarkable ability to project this magnetism and vitality into his music. "He bubbled just as much as his music does," says Harold Arlen. "That is why I believe that anyone who knows George's work, knows George. The humour, the satire, the playfulness of most of his melodic phrases were the natural expression of the man."

In his short life, Gershwin achieved not only commercial success as a popular songwriter but also gained wide acceptance for his influential concert works. His first biographer, Isaac Goldberg, referred in 1931 to "the young colossus bestriding American music, with one foot in Tin Pan Alley, and the other in Carnegie Hall." Since then, George Gershwin has been the subject of numerous articles and biographies. In many of them, the part played by Ira Gershwin in his brother's career has been rather taken for granted, yet they are complementary figures in the evolution of the musical theatre, quite apart from the outstanding merits of their individual songs.

Ira, born 6 December 1896, was the first child of Moishe (Morris) Gershovitz and Rose Bruskin, who had emigrated to the United States in the early 1890s. His parents had first met in St Petersburg but they did not marry until 1895. George was born in Brooklyn, New York, on 26 September 1898. Arthur followed him in 1900, and Frances, the only daughter, was born in 1906. By that time the family had adopted the name of Gershwin and had settled in Manhattan, although settled is hardly the correct word—the family moved home twenty-five times on the lower East Side of New York before George was eighteen.

In his early years, music held little meaning for George. He was an outgoing, mischievous child, who came to be considered the roller-skating champion of his district. Nevertheless, he remembered being deeply affected at the age of six upon hearing an automatic piano leaping through Rubinstein's 'Melody In F'. His most significant boyhood musical experience was when, aged ten, he heard a fellow pupil, Maxie Rosenweig, who later became the noted violinist Max Rosen, playing Dvořák's 'Humoresque'. "It was, to me, a flashing revelation of beauty," Gershwin later recalled.

When he was twelve an upright piano came into the Gershwin home. It had been intended for Ira, but George soon appropriated it for his own use. He amazed the family by his ability to play simple pieces for, unknown to them, he had already been experimenting on a friend's piano.

Ira pursued his own interests. In contrast to the restless, physically active George, he appeared slow-moving, shy and withdrawn. His alert mind delighted in the whimsical and exotic and his favourite childhood occupation was reading.

George began taking lessons from local piano teachers. Charles Hambitzer was the only one who proved satisfactory. Gershwin never hesitated to profess his indebtedness to Hambitzer, who not only improved George's piano technique but also awakened his pupil's interest in the music of such masters as Chopin, Liszt, Debussy and Ravel. In a letter to his sister, Hambitzer referred to Gershwin as a ". . . pupil who will make his mark in music if anybody will. This boy is a genius, without doubt; he's just crazy about music and can't wait until it's time to take his lessons. No watching the clock for this boy. He wants to go in for this modern stuff, jazz and what-not. But I'm not going to let him for a while. I'll see that he gets a firm foundation in the standard music first."

Hambitzer encouraged George to attend concerts, although his pupil was becoming infatuated by jazz and popular music. By 1914, George had already written songs, played popular music at a summer resort and performed a piano solo of his own in public.

After graduating from his school, George enrolled at the High School of Commerce. The uniformly bad marks he received for business studies eventually persuaded his mother that he should be allowed to take the

Ira & George Gershwin

job he had been offered by Remick's, the music publishers. He was engaged as a demonstration pianist and song-plugger at a salary of fifteen dollars a week. At the age of fifteen he was surely the youngest-ever pianist to join a "professional department" in the popular-song business.

Years later Gershwin remembered: "Every day at nine o'clock I was there at the piano, playing popular tunes for anybody who came along. Coloured people used to come in and get me to play 'God Send You Back To Me' in seven keys. Chorus ladies used to breathe down my neck. Some of the customers treated one like dirt."

Nevertheless, those long hours at the piano did wonders for his technique and many professionals sought him out, for he came to be regarded as the finest pianist at Remick's. His own compositions were not appreciated by his employers, however, and in 1916 he signed his first songwriting contract with another firm. His first published song boasted his longest title: 'When You Want 'Em, You Can't Get 'Em, When You Got 'Em, You Don't Want 'Em.' In the same year a Gershwin song was heard for the first time in a Broadway production, when Sigmund Romberg used 'Making Of A Girl' in "The Passing Show Of 1916".

The Broadway theatre, in fact, had become his goal. He heard some songs by Jerome Kern at the wedding of his Aunt Kate and was captivated by them. "Kern was the first composer who made me conscious that most popular music was of inferior quality and that musical-comedy music was made of better material."

After leaving Remick's early in 1917, Gershwin applied for a job as arranger for Irving Berlin, another of his idols. Berlin was impressed by Gershwin's musical gifts, offered him the job but at the same time advised him not to accept it, perceiving that it might have a stifling effect on his talent.

Although flattered by the offer of a high salary from one of his favourite songwriters, Gershwin had the courage to turn down the job. Instead, he eventually obtained work as rehearsal pianist for "Miss 1917", a Broadway musical comedy, enabling him to observe the backstage workings; he was also brought into contact with his idol Kern, Victor Herbert, Florenz Ziegfeld, P. G. Wodehouse, Vivienne Segal, Lew Fields and other notables of the theatre. The manager of "Miss 1917", Harry Askins, brought George to the attention of Max Dreyfus (1874–1964), the "dean of American music publishers", who had a remarkable gift for recognising and sponsoring the potential talent of such writers as Kern, Romberg, Youmans, Porter and Rodgers.

Dreyfus engaged Gershwin as a staff composer for Harms. His only duty was to submit songs to that company for consideration. Through the influence of Dreyfus, Gershwin also obtained more work as a rehearsal pianist. In 1918, 'Some Wonderful Sort Of Someone' was the first Gershwin song to be published by Dreyfus. It was interpolated in "Ladies First". The same show briefly featured 'The Real American Folk Song', with a lyric by "Arthur Francis", the pseudonym of Ira Gershwin. It was the first songwriting collaboration by the brothers to be performed in public.

The Gershwins also collaborated on the songs for a revue, "Half Past Eight", but this closed before reaching Broadway. George's desire to write a complete score for Broadway was at last realised in 1919, when "La, La, Lucille" opened in New York, with lyrics by Arthur Jackson and B. G. De Sylva. It ran for 104 performances.

Gershwin continued to have songs added to shows and "The Capitol Revue" contained 'Swanee', with a lyric by Iving Caesar, the first of his songs to become a worldwide hit. Al Jolson heard Gershwin play 'Swanee' at a party and was so impressed by its vigour that he promoted the song. By the end of 1920, the sheet music and record royalties had earned Gershwin and Caesar over 10,000 dollars.

Gershwin became known to an ever-widening circle of influential acquaintances and at parties his extra-

Dorothy Dandridge & Sidney Poitier in "Porgy and Bess"
Columbia—1959

ordinary facility at the piano made him the centre of attention. Women found him attractive and he was frequently seen with "statuesque, busty show-business types". He seemed to thrive on their adulation.

Nothing, however, was allowed to hinder his career. Ira Gershwin has written that he does not recall any period in his brother's life when George was not trying to further his academic studies. To improve his piano technique and knowledge of harmony, counterpoint and orchestration, he was to study intermittently with Rubin Goldmark, Henry Cowell, Joseph Schillinger and Edward Kilenyi, among others. No matter how occupied he was with theatre or film work, he would always find time to take lessons or to analyse the scores of composers he admired.

From 1920 to 1924, Gershwin wrote the music for five of George White's "Scandals". The stirring 'I'll Build A Stairway To Paradise' was included in the 1922 edition. 'Somebody Loves Me', still a great favourite with musicians who get together to "jam", found a place in the 1924 "Scandals"

"George White's Scandals of 1922" brought Gershwin into contact with Paul Whiteman, the so-called "King of Jazz", who conducted the pit orchestra. On the first night he conducted a performance of Gershwin's twenty-five minute, one-act opera, "Blue Monday", subsequently known as "135th Street". George White thought the piece too gloomy for a light-hearted revue and withdrew it. However, Paul Whiteman was to remember its promise when he planned his famous all-American music concert at New York's Aeolian Hall.

Also in 1922, 'Do It Again', sung by Irene Bordoni with appropriate suggestiveness, titillated the fancy of audiences for "The French Doll". Forty-five years later it was to be prominently featured by Carol Channing in the Universal picture, "Thoroughly Modern Millie", starring Julie Andrews.

Gershwin made his first trip abroad in 1923 to write the music for a London revue, "The Rainbow". He was widely known in Britain through Al Jolson's version of 'Swanee'. With Clifford Grey as lyric-writer he rapidly completed the score of "The Rainbow", which proved to almost as short-lived as the natural phenomena it was named after. The action of the leading comedian on the first night at the Empire Theatre on 3 April 1923 was disastrous for the show. Stepping out of character in the finale he delivered a tirade, complaining that American actors were being employed instead of British ones.

Nineteen twenty-four was a momentous year for Gershwin. Paul Whiteman had invited him to write a composition for piano and orchestra on a jazz theme. A half-promise was made by Gershwin, busy on the score for "Sweet Little Devil", but it was not until a newspaper announced that he was at work on a "jazz concerto" for a concert little more than a month away that he actually made a start on the celebrated 'Rhapsody In Blue'. Gershwin worked best under pressure and in three weeks had completed what was essentially a two-piano version of the piece. Ferde Grofé, Whiteman's noted arranger, orchestrated the 'Rhapsody' in ten days.

"The drunken whoop of an introduction" from the clarinet, electrified the audience when the 'Rhapsody In Blue' was first performed on 12 February 1924, with Gershwin himself at the piano. Its success was instantaneous and probably no work written in America is as well known. Academics have found it easy to denigrate some structural deficiencies, yet as Leonard Bernstein has pointed out, ". . . what's important is not what's wrong with the 'Rhapsody', but what's right with it." Technical flaws are rendered insignificant by the spontaneity, vitality and melodic content in a genuinely original conception. 'Rhapsody In Blue' compelled the attention of both serious and popular musicians and although "symphonic jazz" could not survive its inherent contradictions, from this point on, Gershwin was to receive consideration as an important serious American composer.

Fred Astaire & Joan Fontaine in "Damsel in Distress"
RKO Radio Pictures—1937

In 1924, Gershwin again visited England, this time to write the score for "Primrose", which starred Heather Thatcher and Leslie Henson. When it opened at London's Winter Garden Theatre on 11 September, it was greeted enthusiastically. The full vocal score was soon issued under the Chappell, London, imprint, the first of such publications for Gershwin musicals.

On his return to New York, Gershwin busied himself with the music for the Alex Aarons and Vincent Freedley production of "Lady, Be Good!". It was the first complete Broadway score that George and Ira Gershwin had been commissioned to write. Fred and Adele Astaire headed the cast of what turned out to be a solid musical comedy hit. The rhythmic virtuosity of songs like 'Oh, Lady, Be Good!', 'Fascinating Rhythm', and 'The Half Of It, Dearie, Blues' did much to help the production to success.

One number, since described as "the best popular song ever written", was dropped from "Lady, Be Good!" before the show reached New York. Lady Mountbatten told Gershwin of her unbounded admiration for the song. He autographed her a copy and on her return to London she made it known to her favourite orchestra, who prepared a special arrangement. Soon nearly every band in London was playing it by ear, before the song's popularity spread to Paris. It was later tried in or considered for other musical comedies but 'The Man I Love' succeeded on its own without the aid of theatrical presentation.

The financial rewards that came to Gershwin for the 'Rhapsody In Blue', "Lady, Be Good!" and other productions enabled him to adopt a new life-style. He bought for his family a large grey-stone house, its floors connected by lift. The entire top floor, complete with Steinway grand, was reserved for his own use. After their marriage in 1926, Ira and his wife were assigned the floor below. The living and dining rooms were on another floor. What had once been a small ballroom on the ground floor became a games-room.

"Tell Me More!" opened in April 1925 and ran for only 32 performances in New York. In an attempt to retrieve its losses on Broadway, the show was quickly refurbished for London. Heather Thatcher and Leslie Henson helped the show to achieve a long run. Gershwin himself came to London to work on the production. About this time he began sketching ideas for a concerto, commissioned by the Symphonic Society of New York.

At the Carnegie Hall on 3 December 1925, the 'Concerto In F' was given its first performance, with Gershwin as soloist and Walter Damrosch conducting. It was the first large-scale composition to be orchestrated by Gershwin himself. In common with his other concert works it received a mixed reception but in recent years the 'Concerto' has been accepted by a large public as containing some of his most scintillating music. The poetic second movement, with its nocturnal atmosphere, reveals a deepening sensitivity.

The 28 December 1925 saw the first night of "Tip-Toes" with the poignant 'Looking For A Boy' and the rhythmic 'That Certain Feeling' among its musical pleasures. Two days later, "Song Of The Flame", containing music by George Gershwin and Herbert Stothart, began its run of 219 performances.

Early in 1926, Gershwin again came to London, this time to help prepare "Lady, Be Good!" for the West End stage. He was the "darling of the Mayfair social set" and was invited to London's most glittering parties. His suits were tailored in Savile Row, he bought his hats at Scott's, and he lived in elegant rooms in Pall Mall. He now enjoyed his London visits and felt at home in the capital, especially after "Lady, Be Good!" endeared itself to British audiences.

He returned to New York in April 1926 and began working with Ira on the songs for "Oh, Kay!". They wrote the chorus of 'Do, Do, Do' in half an hour, it is said. Also written for Gertrude Lawrence to sing in her first American musical comedy was 'Someone To Watch Over Me'. Originally, this standard ballad was intended to be sung as an up-

Fred Astaire and Ginger Rogers in "Shall We Dance?"
RKO Radio Pictures—1937

tempo number, until the brothers decided that it sounded much more appealing when performed slowly.

Eleven other shows, including four musicals, began their runs on 8 November 1926, the same night that "Oh, Kay!" opened on Broadway. They hardly affected "Oh, Kay!" which ran for 256 performances. However, it demonstrates the greater opportunities available for writers to get a start in the theatre at that time, when production costs were much lower.

During rehearsals of "Oh, Kay!", Gershwin found time to read DuBose Heyward's best-selling novel, 'Porgy', and immediately saw the musical possibilities of the plot. He wrote to Heyward and thus sagaciously staked his claim for a future collaboration.

About this time he began to take an intense interest in painting. His taste and judgement in contemporary painting may be considered impressive for he collected works by Derain, Chagall, Picasso, Kandinsky, Gauguin, Modigliani and Rousseau. In 1927 he also discovered that he had a natural talent for drawing and painting, an interest he retained for the remainder of his life.

In December 1926 and January 1927, Gershwin acted as accompanist at concerts given by the French-Peruvian contralto, Marguerite d'Alvarez. Later in 1927 he performed as soloist in the 'Rhapsody In Blue' and the 'Concerto in F'. Also in that year, the 'Preludes for Piano' were published.

The Gershwins' next musical, the first version of "Strike Up The Band", closed before it reached New York, probably because its humorously cynical look at war was not "right" for the period. "Funny Face", however, after much re-writing *en route*, arrived in New York to stay for 244 performances. Starring the Astaires, the score had such irresistible numbers as ''S Wonderful', 'He Loves And She Loves', 'My One and Only', and 'Let's Kiss and Make Up', besides the title song.

"Rosalie", starring the shapely Marilyn Miller, stayed on Broadway even longer—335 performances. 'How Long Has This Been Going On?' is the song that

means most to us now, although strangely enough, this was a reject from "Funny Face". To its undoubted advantage, this beautifully constructed song is now sung much more slowly than originally intended.

Gershwin left for what was to be his last European holiday early in 1928, accompanied by his sister Frances and Ira and his wife. Their first stop was London, where George renewed old acquaintances, resumed party-going and mixed with royalty. He also saw Gertrude Lawrence in the final London performance of "Oh, Kay!".

On arrival in Paris he was besieged with invitations and followed by pressmen. There were contacts with Prokofiev, Milhaud, Ravel, Poulenc, Nadia Boulanger, and other leading musicians. Nevertheless, he found time to continue work on 'An American In Paris', completing most of the famous "blues" section. The Gershwin party also visited Berlin and Vienna, where George met Alban Berg, Emmerich Kálmán and Franz Lehár. But wherever Gershwin went he was sure to hear the 'Rhapsody In Blue' played in his honour.

Back in New York in June, the Gershwin brothers prepared the songs for "Treasure Girl". When it opened in November with Gertrude Lawrence in the lead, the reviewers were particularly hard on the plot; the show only achieved 68 performances. 'I've Got A Crush On You' was to become popular, years later, with a "slowly with feeling" rendition far removed from its original "hot" tempo interpretation.

On 13 December 1928, 'An American In Paris' was first performed by the New York Philharmonic conducted by Walter Damrosch at Carnegie Hall. The work soon became firmly entrenched in the orchestral repertory and the usual morning after carpings by the critics now seem irrelevant. The quality of its themes and not its structural organisation has led to its acceptance. As Leonard Bernstein observes, "What's good in it is so good it's irresistible."

'An American In Paris' was included as a ballet in

Georges Guetary in "An American in Paris" MGM—1951

the 1929 Ziegfeld musical, "Show Girl". For this production Ira collaborated with Gus Kahn on the lyrics. 'Liza' is the best-known song, written simply because Ziegfeld wanted a minstrel number with "one hundred beautiful girls seated on steps that cover the entire stage", while Ruby Keeler sang. Ziegfeld blamed Gershwin for the comparative failure of "Show Girl", although over-production seems the more likely reason.

Producer Edgar Selwyn had not given up with "Strike Up The Band". In a version more acceptable to the public he brought the show to New York in January 1930. "I've Got A Crush On You" was added to a score that was more integrated with the plot than previous Gershwin scores had been. Considering that the stock market crash came in October 1929, the run of 191 performances was quite respectable.

George Gershwin's devotion to the piano and his commandeering of that instrument at parties is well known. Nearly always the guests were only too pleased to listen to his brilliant improvisations and there was soon a demand for them in printed form. Originally entitled 'George Gershwin's Song Book', his transcriptions for piano of his own favourite songs were later published in a Chappell edition, retitled 'Gershwin At The Keyboard'.

Many of Gershwin's best ideas apparently came to him at the piano. His creative processes were stimulated as he struck a series of random chords and often a melodic line would emerge guided by his fine harmonic sense. In the early years of the Gershwin brothers' collaboration, the music was usually written first, by George. Then Ira would proceed to fashion his words to fit the melodies with a "glovelike fidelity". A more give-and-take method was evolved in later years. DuBose Heyward related that when working on "Porgy And Bess", he would send scenes and lyrics to the Gershwins, who ". . . after their extraordinary fashion would get at the piano, pound, wrangle, sweat, burst into weird snatches of song, and eventually

emergy with a polished lyric."

In the autumn of 1930, "Girl Crazy" demonstrated that the Gershwin brothers were back on top form. There were romantic hit songs like 'Embraceable You' and 'But Not For Me' sung by the nineteen-year-old Ginger Rogers, and Ethel Merman made an impact in her stage début with the more direct 'I Got Rhythm'. A quartet of rustics sang 'Bidin' My Time', a refreshing take-off on Western ballads and Tin Pan Alley. Incidentally, the orchestra playing in the pit deserves a footnote in jazz history; its members included Benny Goodman, Red Nichols, Gene Krupa and Glenn Miller.

Hollywood called upon the services of the Gershwins in 1931 to write the score for the musical film, "Delicious". Their contract guaranteed a combined salary of a hundred thousand dollars. George, always adept at combining business with pleasure, played tennis and golf and went swimming and hiking between composing. When "Delicious" was released in December 1931, it received a roasting from the critics.

Gershwin salvaged a short orchestral sequence from the film, at first called 'Rhapsody In Rivets', and developed it into the 'Second Rhapsody' for orchestra with piano. Despite its technical advances, most of the critics reactions worried Gershwin when Koussevitzky conducted the first performance in January 1932. Before, they had complained about his craftsmanship; now they complained about a lack of *élan*.

The critics, however, had been completely on his side when "Of Thee I Sing" opened on Broadway in December 1931. In this longest running of Gershwin musicals (441 performances), there was a greater unity between score, dialogue and stage action than anything before. It was the first musical to be awarded a Pulitzer prize.

Gershwin wrote his 'Cuban Overture' for orchestra after a brief stay in Havana. He had been studying Joseph Schillinger's methods of composition, which added a mathematical richness to his orchestration. It

Gene Kelly & Leslie Caron in "An American in Paris"
MGM—1951

was first performed in August 1932 by the New York Philharmonic.

In 1933, "Pardon My English" proved a failure and "Let 'Em Eat Cake", a sequel to "Of Thee I Sing", was too astringent for both critics and public, even though Gershwin felt that it was his best work to date for the stage.

Gershwin's most ambitious undertaking, "Porgy And Bess", was begun late in 1933 and has come to be regarded as his masterwork. He started setting DuBose Heyward's "Porgy" to music, with the author himself as librettist. Following the première of the 'I Got Rhythm Variations' for piano and orchestra and after he had fulfilled a commitment to compère a New York-based radio programme called "Music By Gershwin", the composer went south. He stayed at Folly Beach, South Carolina, where the Heywards had a summer home, and rented a four-room cottage. Here he could observe the blacks in close proximity, especially the Gullahs who retained much of their African heritage. In their worship they attained a state of divine abandonment, chanting or "shouting" to a complex pattern of stamping feet and clapping hands. On one occasion, to Heyward's surprise, Gershwin, without a trace of self-consciousness began shouting with them. He even stole the show from the champion "shouter", much to the Gullahs' delight.

Far from the various pressures of New York, and beyond the reaches of sophistication, with a three-days' growth of beard and wearing only a swim-suit, Gershwin soaked up the atmosphere and the sun. On a battered piano he pounded out the melodies, putting all his enthusiasm into the work of creation. There was a greater depth in his work and Gershwin knew it. He was filled with an "almost mystical wonder at what he was achieving", scarcely believing that he could have written such "marvellous music".

Gershwin returned to New York with the huge task of orchestration and six weeks of rehearsals before him. Four days after his thirty-seventh birthday "Porgy And Bess" opened in Boston. Ten days later on 10 October 1935, billed as "An American Folk Opera" with an hour clipped from the running time, this poetic folk tale of the crippled beggar and the "seething life of Catfish Row", opened at New York's Alvin Theatre. The critics, with their penchant for classification, had difficulty in deciding what "Porgy And Bess" really was, although one or two discerned the unquestionable advance in Gershwin's art.

Its initial run of 124 performances was remarkable for a new opera but a sixteen weeks' run was a flop by Broadway standards. "Porgy and Bess' was a commercial failure, although revivals have since become big business. The songs, including 'Summertime', 'I Got Plenty O' Nuttin' ', 'It Ain't Necessarily So' and 'Bess, You Is My Woman', quickly won great popularity; full recognition of Gershwin's total achievement came only after his death. The hand of the craftsman is shown in his masterly control of the elements of song, orchestral colour and dramatic mood, evident in scene after scene.

Broadway may have been Gershwin's first love, but three flops in a row dictated that he and his brother should go west to Hollywood. In 1936 they were to contribute only one song, 'By Strauss', a witty take-off on the Viennese waltz, to a Broadway production. In August they leased a Spanish-style house in Beverly Hills. Old friends like Irving Berlin and Jerome Kern were already in Hollywood and Gershwin soon became friendly with Arnold Schoenberg, the "twelve-tone" composer, with whom he shared a love of tennis. Parties and dinners were enjoyed by Gershwin on most evenings and he usually required little persuasion before entertaining himself and other guests at the piano.

RKO were so impressed by 'They Can't Take That Away From Me', 'They All Laughed' and 'Let's Call The Whole Thing Off', which the Gershwins wrote for "Shall We Dance?", that they were assigned to work on the next Astaire picture.

Mickey Rooney & Judy Garland in "Girl Crazy"
MGM—1943

George Gershwin developed showmanship, and also supplemented his income, by performing his concert works to usually packed and enthralled audiences. It was while appearing as piano soloist in the 'Concerto In F' with the Los Angeles Philharmonic in February 1937, that he experienced the first portent of his fatal illness. He momentarily lost consciousness and stumbled over an easy passage during the first movement and he again suffered a mental lapse while playing the coda. Nothing like this had happened to him before. After the next concert he complained that, while conducting, he had experienced a blinding headache, somehow associated in his mind with an acrid smell like burning rubber.

A medical check-up revealed nothing physically wrong and these incidents were soon forgotten as he continued working with Ira on the songs for "A Damsel In Distress", in which Joan Fontaine took the place of Ginger Rogers as Fred Astaire's partner. The songs, such as 'A Foggy Day' and 'Nice Work If You Can Get It' were vintage Gershwin.

The gossip columnists enjoyed themselves with their real or imagined stories of George's amours as he carried on wholeheartedly working and playing. In May, he and Ira started work on "The Goldwyn Follies".

By early June, George began to complain more frequently of headaches and dizzy spells. The normally ebullient Gershwin became listless and it was obvious that he was seriously ill. When his condition rapidly deteriorated on 9 July, he was rushed to hospital—a brain tumour now suspected. Frantic attempts were made to locate a famous brain specialist, who was on a yachting holiday. When he was finally contacted it proved too late for him to be flown to Hollywood; Gershwin's pulse rate was so low that an immediate operation was imperative. The preliminary surgery lasted for an hour-and-a-half and the major operation for another four hours.

George Gershwin never regained consciousness. He died the following morning, 11 July 1937, at the age of thirty-eight. The specialists were in agreement that even if it had been possible to remove the tumour completely, it would have recurred in a short time, supposing that he had survived the operation.

The news was greeted with dismay and shock around the world. The tributes poured in. It is futile to speculate on what he might have written had he lived. The four songs that were used in his last film, "The Goldwyn Follies", show him to have been at the height of his powers as a melodist. They include 'Love Is Here To Stay' and 'Love Walked In'. Ira Gershwin has written that 'Love Is Here To Stay' was the last song that George worked on. It became even more popular after the 1951 MGM film, "An American In Paris".

In 1946, with the musical help of Kay Swift, Ira fashioned a number of unpublished songs into a fine film score for "The Shocking Miss Pilgrim", including the tender 'For You, For Me, For Evermore'. He was also able to revamp material for the 1964 Billy Wilder film production, "Kiss Me, Stupid".

After he had recovered from the shock of his brother's death, Ira worked successfully with Jerome Kern, Kurt Weill, Harry Warren and Harold Arlen. His lyric-writing skill remained undiminished as attested by such fine songs as, 'Long Ago And Far Away', 'Jenny', 'My Ship' and 'The Man That Got Away'. For the past few decades, Ira Gershwin has been kept busy annotating Gershwin material for the Library of Congress and looking after the business side of matters Gershwin.

Although he and his brother were as unalike as two brothers could be, together they formed a complementary team, bringing gaiety and pleasure to millions living between two world wars. It must be a source of satisfaction to him that the brother he so admired is far from being forgotten. Today, George Gershwin's music is played, sung and recorded even more frequently than it was in his brief lifetime.

SWANEE
"Capitol Revue"

DO IT AGAIN
"The French Doll"

I'LL BUILD A STAIRWAY TO PARADISE
"George White's Scandals of 1922"

SOMEBODY LOVES ME
"George White's Scandals of 1924"

CAPITOL REVUE. Capital Theatre, New York, 24 October 1919.

THE FRENCH DOLL. Comedy adapted from the French of ARMONT and GERHEDON by A. E. THOMAS. Produced by E. RAY GOETZ at the Lyceum Theatre, New York, 20 February 1922. 120 performances. Cast included IRENE BORDONI, THURSTON HALL and EDNA HIBBARD.

GEORGE WHITE'S SCANDALS OF 1924. Lyrics by B. G. DESYLVA. Book by WILLIAM K. WELLS and GEORGE WHITE. Produced by GEORGE WHITE at the Apollo Theatre, New York, 30 June 1924. 192 performances. Cast included WINNIE LIGHTNER, TOM PATRICOLA, the ELM CITY FOUR, the WILLIAMS SISTERS, LESTER ALLEN, RICHARD BOLD, WILL MAHONEY and HELEN HUDSON.

GEORGE WHITE'S SCANDALS OF 1922. Book by GEORGE WHITE and W. C. FIELDS. Produced by GEORGE WHITE at the Globe Theatre, New York, 28 August 1922. 88 performances. Cast included WINNIE LIGHTNER, JACK MCGOWAN, GEORGE WHITE, PEARL REGAY, W. C. FIELDS, LESTER ALLEN and PAUL WHITEMAN's orchestra.

SWANEE
"Capitol Revue"

by GEORGE GERSHWIN,
IRVING CAESAR and IRA GERSHWIN

DO IT AGAIN
"The French Doll"

by GEORGE GERSHWIN,
B.G. DE SYLVA and IRA GERSHWIN

(I'LL BUILD A) STAIRWAY TO PARADISE

"George White's Scandals of 1922"

by GEORGE GERSHWIN, ARTHUR FRANCIS
and B.G. DE SYLVA

- bove it's so fair. Shoes! Go on and car-ry me there!

I'll build a stair-way to Pa-ra-dise With a new step ev-'ry

day.

day.

SOMEBODY LOVES ME
"George White's Scandals of 1924"

Music and Lyrics by GEORGE GERSHWIN,
BALLARD MacDONALD and B.G. DE SYLVA

SO AM I

ALFRED BUTT
WITH
ALEX A. AARONS AND VINTON FREEDLEY
PRESENT

FRED AND ADELE ASTAIRE
IN

LADY BE GOOD!

The Play Produced by FELIX EDWARDES

BOOK BY
GUY BOLTON
AND
FRED THOMPSON
LYRICS BY
IRA GERSHWIN
MUSIC BY
GEORGE GERSHWIN

Photograph by STRAUSS PAYTON

CHAPPELL & CO. LTD.
50 NEW BOND STREET, LONDON, W.I.
& SYDNEY

HARMS INCORPORATED
62-64 WEST 45TH STREET
NEW YORK

THE MAN I LOVE

OH, LADY, BE GOOD!
"Lady, Be Good!"

FASCINATING RHYTHM
"Lady, Be Good!"

THAT CERTAIN FEELING
"Tip-Toes"

LADY, BE GOOD! Lyrics by IRA GERSHWIN. Book by GUY BOLTON and FRED THOMPSON. Produced by ALEX A. AARONS and VINTON FREEDLEY at the Liberty Theatre, New York, 1 December 1924. 184 performances. Cast included FRED and ADELE ASTAIRE, WALTER CATLETT, CLIFF EDWARDS, GERALD OLIVER SMITH, PATRICIA CLARKE, ALAN EDWARDS, PHIL OHMAN and VICTOR ARDEN at the pianos. (London: Empire Theatre, 14 April 1926.)

TIP-TOES. Lyrics by IRA GERSHWIN. Book by GUY BOLTON and FRED THOMPSON. Produced by ALEX A. AARONS and VINTON FREEDLEY at the Liberty Theatre, New York, 28 December 1925. 192 performances. Cast included QUEENIE SMITH, ALLEN KEARNS, HARRY WATSON JR., ANDREW TOMBES, JEANETTE MACDONALD, LOVEY LEE, AMY REVERE and ROBERT HALLIDAY, with PHIL OHMAN and VICTOR ARDEN at the pianos. (London: Winter Garden, 31 August 1926.)

THE MAN I LOVE
"Lady, Be Good!"

Music and Lyrics by
GEORGE GERSHWIN and IRA GERSHWIN

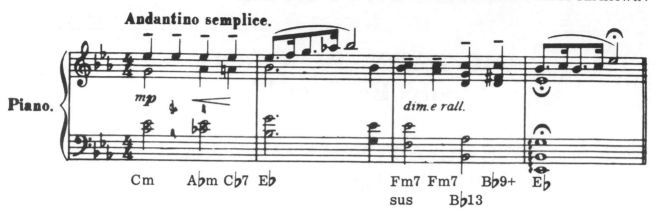

he for me. Al - though I re - al - ize as well as you,

Eb   Cm7 C+   F9   Bb7   Eb   Bb7

It is sel - dom that a dream comes true, To me it's

Gm   Cm   C⁰   Bb

clear   That he'll ap - pear.

dim.   *poco rall.*

F7-9   Bb   Bb⁰/F   Fm7   Bb7

REFRAIN. (*slow*)

OH, LADY, BE GOOD!
"Lady, Be Good!"

Music and Lyrics by
GEORGE GERSHWIN and IRA GERSHWIN

1. Lis - ten to my tale of woe, It's ter - ri - bly sad, but true.
2. Au - burn and bru - nette and blonde, I love 'em all, tall or small.

All dressed up, no place to go, Each
But some - how they don't grow fond, They

FASCINATING RHYTHM
"Lady, Be Good!"

Music and Lyrics by
GEORGE GERSHWIN and IRA GERSHWIN

THAT CERTAIN FEELING
"Tip-Toes"

Music and Lyrics by
GEORGE GERSHWIN and IRA GERSHWIN

47

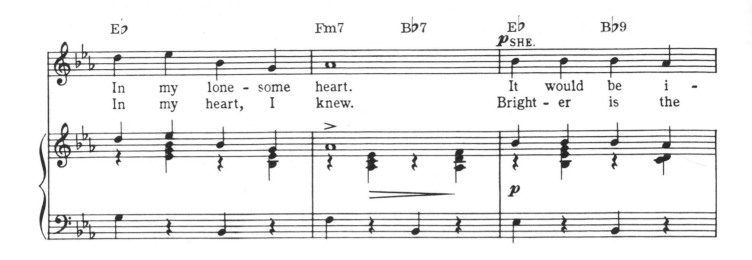

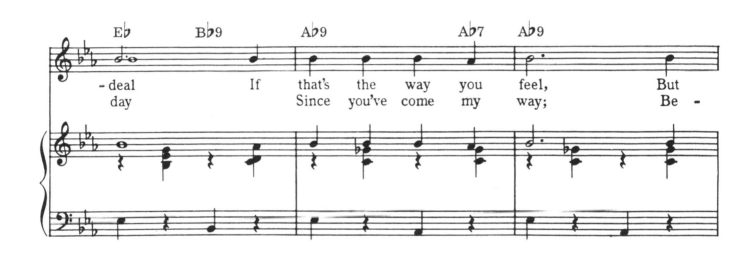

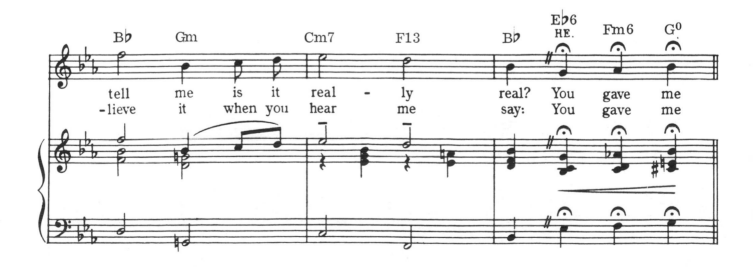

DO, DO, DO
"Oh, Kay!"

SOMEONE TO WATCH OVER ME
"Oh, Kay!"

'S WONDERFUL
"Funny Face"

HOW LONG HAS THIS BEEN GOING ON?
"Rosalie"

OH, KAY! Lyrics by IRA GERSHWIN. Book by GUY BOLTON and P. G. WODEHOUSE. Produced by ALEX A. AARONS and VINTON FREEDLEY at the Imperial Theatre, New York, 8 November 1926. 256 performances. Cast included GERTRUDE LAWRENCE, OSCAR SHAW, VICTOR MOORE, HARLAND DIXON, and the FAIRBANKS TWINS. PHIL OHMAN AND VICTOR ARDEN at the pianos.
(London: His Majesty's, 21 September 1927.)

FUNNY FACE. Lyrics by IRA GERSHWIN. Book by FRED THOMPSON and PAUL GERARD SMITH. Produced by ALEX A. AARONS and VINTON FREEDLEY at the Alvin Theatre, New York, 22 November 1927. 244 performances. Cast included FRED AND ADELE ASTAIRE, ALLEN KEARNS, VICTOR MOORE, WILLIAM KENT and BETTY COMPTON. PHIL OHMAN and VICTOR ARDEN at the pianos.
(London: Prince's, 8 November 1928.)
[Film version: Paramount 1957.]

ROSALIE. Book by WILLIAM ANTHONY MCGUIRE and GUY BOLTON. Produced by FLORENZ ZIEGFELD at the New Amsterdam Theatre, New York, 10 January 1928. 335 performances. Cast included MARILYN MILLER, JACK DONAHUE, GLADYS GLAD, FRANK MORGAN, BOBBE ARNST. SIGMUND ROMBERG collaborated on the score.

DO, DO, DO
"Oh, Kay!"

Music and Lyrics by
GEORGE GERSHWIN and IRA GERSHWIN

SOMEONE TO WATCH OVER ME

"Oh, Kay!"

Music and Lyrics by
GEORGE GERSHWIN and IRA GERSHWIN

'S WONDERFUL
"Funny Face"

Music and Lyrics by
GEORGE GERSHWIN and IRA GERSHWIN

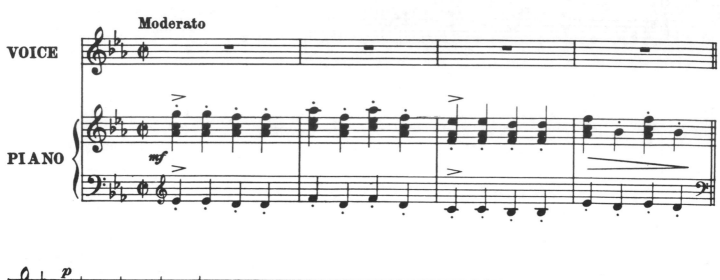

1. (HE) Life has just be - gun,   Jack has found his   Jill;
2. (SHE) Don't mind tell - ing you,   In my hum - ble   fash,

Don't know what you've done,   But I'm all a - thrill.
That you thrill me through   With a ten - der pash.

REFRAIN

HOW LONG HAS THIS BEEN GOING ON?

"Rosalie"

Music and Lyrics by
GEORGE GERSHWIN and IRA GERSHWIN

Bill: As a tot, when I trot-ted in lit-tle vel-vet pant-ies,—
Mary: 'Neath the stars at ba-zaars of-ten I've had to ca-ress men,—

I was kissed by my sis-ters, my cous-ins and my aun-ties.—
Five or ten dol-lars then I'd col-lect from all those yes-men.—

Sad to tell, it was Hell, an in-fer-no worse than Dan-te's.—
Don't be sad, I must add that they meant no more than chess-men.—

So, my dear, I swore,— "Nev - er, nev - er - more!"
Dar - ling, can't you see — 'Twas for char - it - y.

On my list I in - sis - ted that kiss - ing must be crossed out.—
Though these lips have made slips, it was nev - er real - ly se - rious,—

Now I find I was blind, and oh la - dy, how I've lost out!—
Who'd a'thought I'd be brought to a state that's so de - li - rious?—

Refrain
I could cry — salt - y tears;— Where have I been all these years?—
I could cry— salt - y tears;— Where have I been all these years?—

LIZA
"Show Girl"

BUT NOT FOR ME
"Girl Crazy"

EMBRACEABLE YOU
"Girl Crazy"

BIDIN' MY TIME
"Girl Crazy"

I GOT RHYTHM
"Girl Crazy"

SHOW GIRL. Lyrics by GUS KAHN and IRA GERSHWIN. Book by WILLIAM ANTHONY McGUIRE and J. P. McEVOY. Produced by FLORENZ ZIEGFELD at the Ziegfeld Theatre, New York, 2 July 1929. 111 performances. Cast included RUBY KEELER, AL JOLSON, EDDIE FOY JR., FRANK McHUGH, JIMMY DURANTE, LOU CLAYTON, EDDIE JACKSON, BARBARA NEWBERRY and HARRIET HOCTOR.

GIRL CRAZY. Lyrics by IRA GERSHWIN. Book by GUY BOLTON and JOHN McGOWAN. Produced by ALEX A. AARONS and VINTON FREEDLEY at the Alvin Theatre, New York, 14 October 1930. 272 performances. Cast included GINGER ROGERS, ALLEN KEARNS, WILLIAM KENT, WILLIE HOWARD, ETHEL MERMAN and the RED NICHOLS BAND.
(Film versions: RKO 1932; MGM 1943; MGM "When The Boys Meet The Girls" 1965.)

LIZA
(All The Clouds'll Roll Away)
"Show Girl"

by GEORGE GERSHWIN, GUS KAHN
and IRA GERSHWIN

BUT NOT FOR ME
"Girl Crazy"

Music and Lyrics by
GEORGE GERSHWIN and IRA GERSHWIN

REFRAIN Rather slow *(smoothly)*

EMBRACEABLE YOU
"Girl Crazy"

Music and Lyrics by
GEORGE GERSHWIN and IRA GERSHWIN

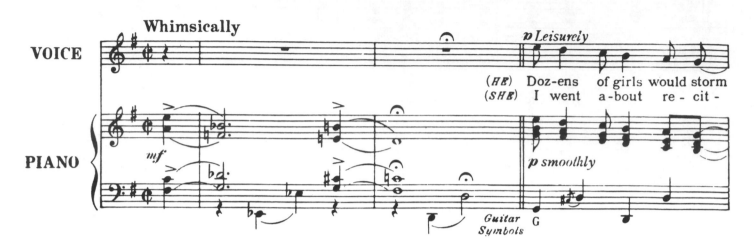

REFRAIN (*Rhythmically*)

BIDIN' MY TIME
"Girl Crazy"

Music and Lyrics by
GEORGE GERSHWIN and IRA GERSHWIN

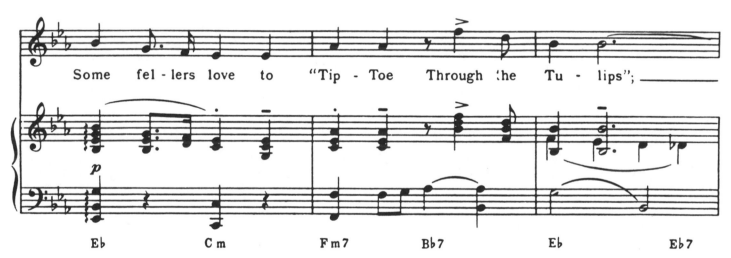

Some fel-lers love to "Tip - Toe Through the Tu - lips";

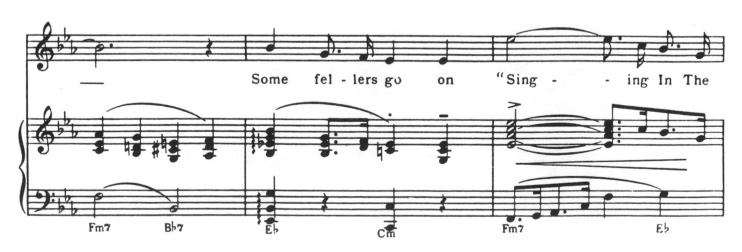

Some fel-lers go on "Sing - -ing In The

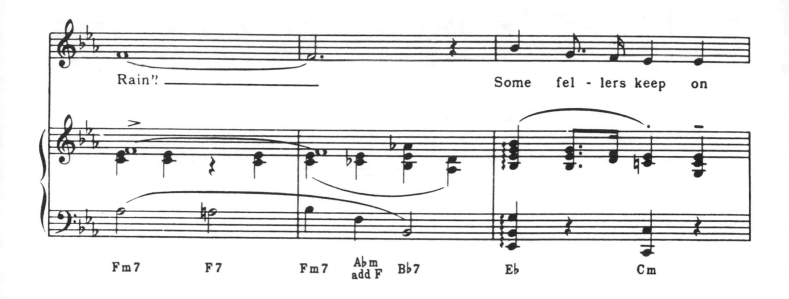

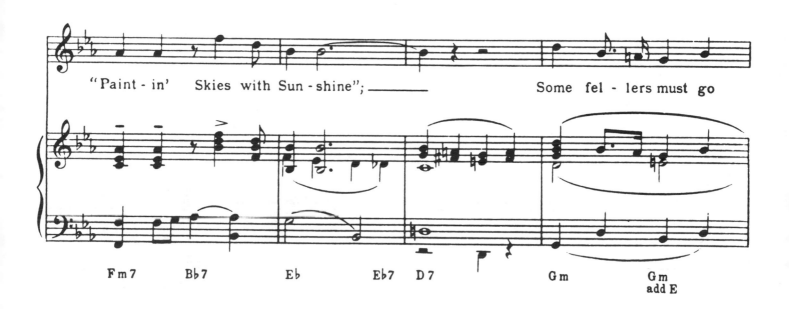

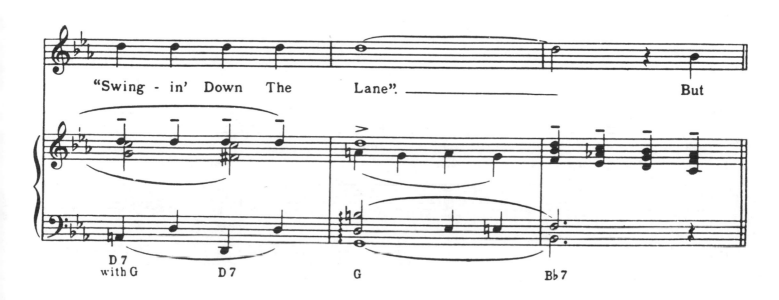

I GOT RHYTHM
"Girl Crazy"

Music and Lyrics by
GEORGE GERSHWIN and IRA GERSHWIN

REFRAIN *(with abandon)*

SUMMERTIME
"Porgy And Bess"

IT AIN'T NECESSARILY SO
"Porgy And Bess"

BESS, YOU IS MY WOMAN
"Porgy And Bess"

I GOT PLENTY O' NUTTIN'
"Porgy And Bess"

BY STRAUSS
"The Show Is On"

LET'S CALL THE WHOLE THING OFF
"Shall We Dance"

THEY CAN'T TAKE THAT AWAY FROM ME
"Shall We Dance"

THEY ALL LAUGHED
"Shall We Dance"

PORGY AND BESS. Lyrics by DuBose Heyward and Ira Gershwin. Libretto by DuBose Heyward. Produced by the Theatre Guild at the Alvin Theatre, New York, 10 October 1935. 124 performances. Cast included Todd Duncan (Porgy), Anne Brown (Bess), John W. Bubbles (Sportin' Life), Warren Coleman (Crown), Ruby Elzy (Serena), Abbie Mitchell (Clara), Eddie Matthews (Jake), Georgette Harvey (Maria), J. Rosamond Johnson (Frazier), Helen Dowdy (Lily, and Strawberry Woman), Ray Yeates (Nelson, and Crab Man), Ford L. Buck (Mingo), Gus Simons (Peter) and the Eva Jessye Choir.

SHALL WE DANCE? Lyrics by Ira Gershwin. Screenplay by Allan Scott and Ernest Pagano. Produced by Pandro S. Berman. Released by RKO, 7 May 1937. Cast included Fred Astaire, Ginger Rogers, Edward Everett Horton, Eric Blore, Jerome Cowan and Harriet Hoctor.

SUMMERTIME
"Porgy And Bess"

by GEORGE GERSHWIN, DUBOSE and DOROTHY HEYWARD
and IRA GERSHWIN

IT AIN'T NECESSARILY SO
"Porgy And Bess"

by GEORGE GERSHWIN, DUBOSE and DOROTHY HEYWARD
and IRA GERSHWIN

BESS, YOU IS MY WOMAN
"Porgy And Bess"

by GEORGE GERSHWIN, DUBOSE and DOROTHY HEYWARD
and IRA GERSHWIN

I GOT PLENTY O' NUTTIN'
"Porgy And Bess"

by GEORGE GERSHWIN, DUBOSE and DOROTHY HEYWARD
and IRA GERSHWIN

BY STRAUSS
"The Show Is On"

Music and Lyrics by
GEORGE GERSHWIN and IRA GERSHWIN

Oh, I'd give no quar-ter to Kern or Cole Por-ter and Gersh-win keeps pound-ing on tin. _____ How can I be civ-il when hear-ing this driv-el? It's on-ly for night club-bing sous-es. _____ Oh, give me the free 'n' eas-y

waltz that is Vi - en - nese - y   And   go tell the band   if

they want a hand   the   waltz must be Strauss's!

Ya,   ya,   ya! _____   Give me

oom - pah - pah! _____

mp grazioso

rall.

f marcato

LET'S CALL THE WHOLE THING OFF

"Shall We Dance?"

Music and Lyrics by
GEORGE GERSHWIN and IRA GERSHWIN

Allegretto

Piano

mf *poco rit.*

mp Brightly

Things have come to a pret-ty pass,— Our ro-mance is grow-ing flat, For

mp leggiero a tempo

D   B7   Em   A7   D   G9

you like this and the o-ther — While I go for this and that.

C#7 +5   F#7   B7   D (E Bass)   E9   E-9   A7

mp

Goodness knows what the end will be;— Oh, I don't know where I'm at — It looks as if we

mp

D   B7   Em   A7   D   G9   A

two will nev-er be one, Some-thing must be done.

E7   A   C9   A7   D   D7   G   D7

REFRAIN

You say ee - ther And I say eye-ther, You say nee-ther And I say ny - ther; Ee - ther, eye-ther,
You say laughter And I say lawf-ter, You say af - ter And I say awf - ter; Laugh-ter, lawf-ter,

G   Em   Am7   D7   G   Em   Am7   D7   G   G7

nee ther, ny-ther, Let's call the whole thing off! You like po-ta-to and I like po-tah-to,
af - ter, awf-ter, Let's call the whole thing off! You like va-nil-la and I like va-nel-la,

C   Cm   G   Em   A7   D7   G   Em   Am7   D7

You like to-ma-to and I like to-mah-to; Po - ta-to, Po-tah-to, To - ma-to, To-mah-to!
You, sa's'- pa-ril-la and I sa's'- pa-rel-la; Va - nil-la, va - nel-la, Choc-late, straw-b'ry!

G   Em   Am7   D7   G   G7   C   Cm6

THEY CAN'T TAKE THAT AWAY FROM ME

"Shall We Dance?"

Music and Lyrics by
GEORGE GERSHWIN and IRA GERSHWIN

REFRAIN *(not fast)*

THEY ALL LAUGHED
"Shall We Dance?"

Music and Lyrics by
GEORGE GERSHWIN and IRA GERSHWIN

REFRAIN (*happily*)

They all laughed at Chris-to-pher Co-lum-bus When he said the World was round.. They all laughed when
They all laughed at Rock-e-fel-ler Cen-ter Now they're fight-ing to get in.___ They all laughed at

G Em Am9 Am D7 Am9 Am Cm6 D13 Bm7 Bb7 Am7 D+G Em

Ed-i-son re-cord-ed sound.___
Whit-ney and his cot-ton gin.___

They all laughed at Wil-bur and his broth-er,
They all laughed at Ful-ton and his steam-boat,

Am9 Am D7 G6 G Em Am7 D7

When they said that man could fly.__
Her-shey and his choc'late bar.__

They told Mar-co-ni Wire-less was a pho-ney; It's the same old
Ford and his Liz-zie Kept the laugh-ers bus-y; That's how peo-ple

C#7+ F#9 F#7+ Bm E9 D6 Bm6 A9(13) A+9 D9 E9 F9 E9

cry. They laughed at me_want-ing you,_ Said I was reach-ing for the moon; But oh,_ You came
are. They laughed at me_want-ing you,_ Said it would be Hel-lo, Good-bye; But oh,_ You came

D9 D7 G9 G G9 Dm6 Em7 Dm6 B+7 E9 E7-9 A7 A9 A D

NICE WORK IF YOU CAN GET IT
"A Damsel In Distress"

A FOGGY DAY
"A Damsel In Distress"

LOVE WALKED IN
"The Goldwyn Follies"

LOVE IS HERE TO STAY
"The Goldwyn Follies"

FOR YOU, FOR ME, FOR EVERMORE
"The Shocking Miss Pilgrim"

A DAMSEL IN DISTRESS. Lyrics by IRA GERSHWIN. Screenplay by P. G. WODEHOUSE, ERNEST PAGANO and S. K. LAUREN. Produced by PANDRO S. BERMAN. Released by RKO, 19 November 1937. Cast included FRED ASTAIRE, GEORGE BURNS, GRACIE ALLEN, JOAN FONTAINE, REGINALD GARDINER and RAY NOBLE.

THE GOLDWYN FOLLIES. Lyrics by IRA GERSHWIN. Screenplay by BEN HECHT. Produced by SAMUEL GOLDWYN. Released by Goldwyn-United Artists, 23 February 1938. Cast included ADOLPHE MENJOU, the RITZ BROTHERS, ZORINA, KENNY BAKER, ANDREA LEEDS, HELEN JEPSON, ELLA LOGAN, PHIL BAKER, BOBBY CLARK, JEROME COWAN, EDGAR BERGEN and CHARLIE McCARTHY.

THE SHOCKING MISS PILGRIM. Lyrics by IRA GERSHWIN. Screenplay by GEORGE SEATON. Produced by WILLIAM PERLBERG. Released by 20th Century-Fox. Cast included BETTY GRABLE, DICK HAYMES, ANNE REVERE, ALLYN JOSLYN and GENE LOCKHART.

NICE WORK IF YOU CAN GET IT

"A Damsel In Distress"

Music and Lyrics by
GEORGE GERSHWIN and IRA GERSHWIN

A FOGGY DAY
"A Damsel In Distress"

Music and Lyrics by
GEORGE GERSHWIN and IRA GERSHWIN

REFRAIN (*brighter but warmly*)

LOVE WALKED IN
"The Goldwyn Follies"

Music and Lyrics by
GEORGE GERSHWIN and IRA GERSHWIN

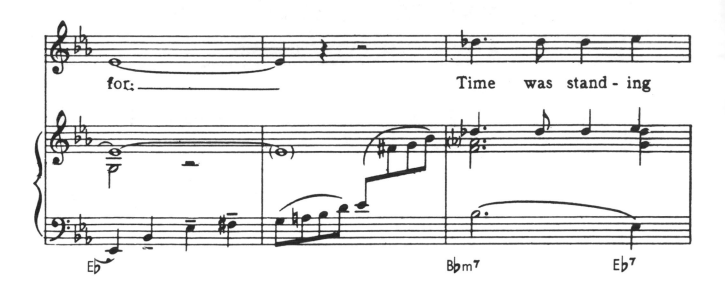

for: _____ Time was stand-ing

still, No one count-ed till There

came a knock-knock-knock-ing at the door. _____

REFRAIN

LOVE IS HERE TO STAY
"The Goldwyn Follies"

Music and Lyrics by
GEORGE GERSHWIN and IRA GERSHWIN

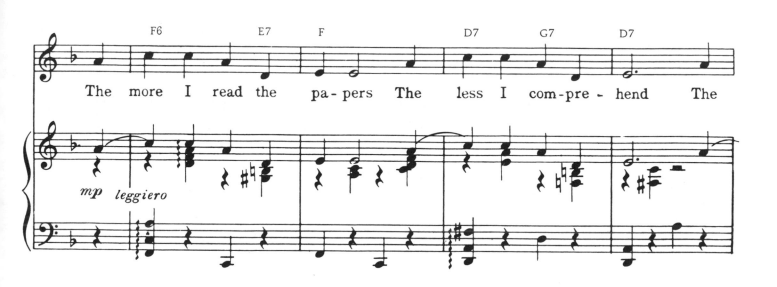

The more I read the pa-pers The less I com-pre-hend The

world and all its ca-pers And how it all will end. Noth-ing seems to be

The ra - di - o and the tel - e - phone and the

mov - ies that we know May just be pass - ing fan - cies,

And in time may go. But, oh my dear,

Our love is here to stay; To - geth - er

FOR YOU, FOR ME, FOR EVERMORE

"The Shocking Miss Pilgrim"

Music and Lyrics by
GEORGE GERSHWIN and IRA GERSHWIN

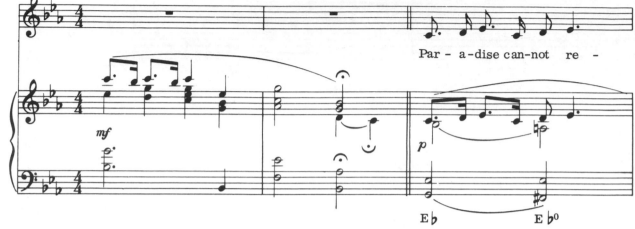

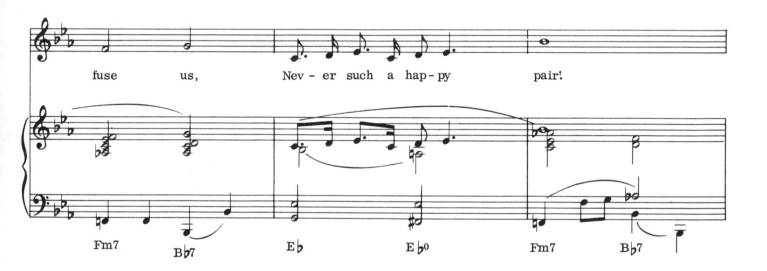

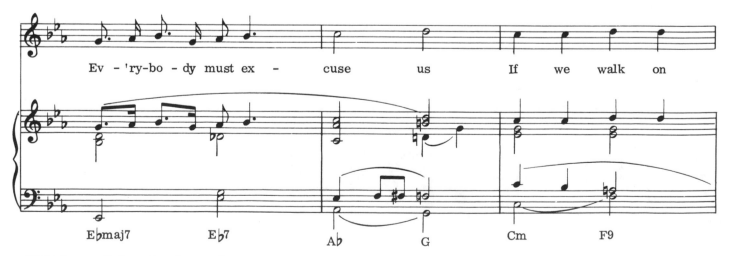